FOLENS SPELLING

REINFORCEMENT ACTIVITIES

BOOK 3

Glendra Read

Folens
Publishers

CONTENTS

© 1994 Folens Limited, on behalf of the author.

First published 1994 by Folens Limited, Dunstable and Dublin.

Editor: Ian Jenkins

Illustrations by Chris Masters   Cover design by Graphic Editions   Cover artwork by Design for Marketing

ISBN 185276582-8   Printed in Singapore by Craft Print.

Folens Limited, Albert House, Apex Business Centre, Boscombe Road, Dunstable, LU5 4RL, England.

INTRODUCTION

Using this book

This book provides reinforcement spelling activities for children working at level three and above of the National Curriculum in English. The activities are designed to remedy the spelling difficulties which have been identified using the *Diagnostic Assessment* books in this series.

The activity sheets are designed to be used as supplementary exercises, or as practice sheets to help children master groups of words which have not been fully learnt. The exercises could be extended, where appropriate, by encouraging children to write words again on the backs of the sheets, or by helping them to look for associated words.

Areas covered include: knowledge of parts of speech; synonyms; silent letters; proofreading practice; polysyllabic words; prefixes and suffixes; abbreviations; apostrophe usage; suggestions for work with a dictionary and a thesaurus; **ei** and **ie**; and word endings. There are six games sheets (including anagrams and wordsearches) and two sheets encouraging vocabulary expansion.

This book and the National Curriculum

At level three of the National Curriculum, children should be confidently spelling words of increasing complexity. They should be aware of the grammatical structures essential for good speaking and writing and should be using capital letters, full stops and question marks correctly and consistently. Written work at this level should be produced in legible joined-up handwriting.

At level four children should be able to spell increasingly complex polysyllabic words, and be aware of the function of nouns, pronouns, adjectives, verbs and adverbs. They should be using different verb tenses consistently and appropriately, and be producing work in fluent and legible handwriting.

At level five children should be able to spell complex polysyllabic words using prefixes and suffixes, and understand the principles of consonant doubling and vowel deletion. They should be punctuating complex sentences correctly and be checking the first draft of their writing both for the accuracy of their spelling and for the presentation of their work.

Ten Rules for Good Writing

1. Write in a clear style appropriate to the audience.
2. Write neatly and present work with care.
3. Write in sentences with correct punctuation.
4. Write in paragraphs, starting a new paragraph for each new idea.
5. Write each new part of direct speech on a new line.
6. Make sure that rules of grammar are observed, e.g. that there is subject-verb agreement.
7. Keep to the point, using appropriate adjectives and adverbs to enliven the work. Use a thesaurus.
8. Check spellings using a dictionary.
9. Bring the writing to a clear ending which is in keeping with the rest of the work.
10. Use a computer to print out work for display, or for a special purpose, e.g. to produce a newspaper.

RESOURCES

Books

1. Alston, J. and Taylor, J. *The Handwriting File*. L.D.A.
2. Bissex, G.L. (1980) *Gnys at Wrk*. Harvard University Press.
3. Brown and Brown (1990) *A Speller's Companion*. Reed's Ltd.
4. Bryant, P.E. and Bradley, L. (1985) *Children's Reading Problems*. Blackwell.
5. Daniels, J.C. and Diack, H. (1979) *The Standard Reading Tests*. Hart-Davis.
6. Gee, R. and Watson, C. (1990) *English Spelling*. Usborne.
7. Gentry, J.R. (1987) *Spel... is a Four Letter Word*. Scholastic.
8. Marsh, E. (1989) *Help yourself to English Spelling*. Oriflamme.
9. McNally, B. and Murray, W. (1970) *Key Words to Literacy*. The Teacher Publishing Company.
10. National Curriculum Documents. *English in the National Curriculum*. H.M.S.O.
11. Peters, M.L. (1975) *Diagnostic and Remedial Spelling Manual*. Macmillan.
12. Schonell, F.J. (1976) *Graded Word Spelling Test*. L.D.A.
13. Torbe, M. (1977) *Teaching Spelling*. Ward Lock Educational.
14. Vernon, P.E. (1977) *Spelling Test*. N.F.E.R. Nelson.
15. Vincent, D. and Claydon, J. (1982) *Diagnostic Spelling Test*. N.F.E.R. Nelson.

Dictionaries and thesauri

1. *A.C.E. Dictionary (Aurally Coded English)* L.D.A.
2. Beeching, C.L. (1989) *A Dictionary of Eponyms*. Oxford University Press.
3. Cohen, J.M. and Cohen, M.J. (1960) *Dictionary of Quotations*. Penguin.
4. Cripps, C. and Peters, M.L. (1991) *Hands on Spelling Dictionary*. L.D.A.
5. Fergusson, R. (1984) *The Penguin Rhyming Dictionary*. Penguin.
6. Fowler, H.W. and Fowler, F.C. (1989) *The Concise Oxford Dictionary*. Oxford.
7. Grisewood, J. (1990) *Fact File Dictionary*. W. H. Smith.
8. Hawkins, J.M. (1991) *New Oxford School Dictionary*. Oxford University Press.
9. *Pergamon Dictionary of Perfect Spelling*. Pergamon.
10. *Pocket Thesaurus*. (1984) Kingfisher Books.
11. Roget, P.M. (1933 edition) *Thesaurus – Classic Edition*. Avenel Books.
12. Spooner A. (1987) *Oxford Children's Thesaurus*. Sphere Books.
13. *Young People's Thesaurus Dictionary*. Ward Lock Educational.

Spelling programmes/workbooks

1. Brand, V. *Spelling Made Easy*. Egon Publishers Ltd.
2. Cripps, C. (1978) *Catchwords - Ideas for Teaching Spelling*. A set of six graded workbooks. HBJ.
3. Dictionaries: A.C.E. (Aurally Coded English) L.D.A.; *Pergamon Dictionary of Perfect Spelling*. Pergamon.
   Both these dictionaries are for children who experience difficulties with spelling. Words can be found according to their sound, e.g., 'psychology' can be found under 'p' and 's'.
4. Hughes, J. *Sounds, Pictures, Words*. Graded workbooks for five to eight year olds. Nelson.
5. Richards, J.P.B.S. (1980) *Attack Spelling Programme*. 100 systematically structured spelling lessons. Nottingham.
6. *Stile Spelling Programme*. Self-correcting spelling programme for five to fourteen year olds. L.D.A.

Spellchecker

Franklin Elementary Spellmaster (QES90). Designed for children, contains 26 800 words. Innovations International Ltd.

Computer programs

1. *Short Vowel Sounds, Magic e, Consonant Blends, Vowel Digraphs, Word Builder*. Five programs to help with phonics. Sherston Software.
2. *Spelling Week by Week*. Six Levels cover the ages five to eleven. The computer monitors and scores levels for each child. Chalksoft Ltd.
3. *Star Spell* (for younger children) and *Star Spell Plus* (for older children). Fisher Marriott.

Name _____   Date _____

Nouns

Nouns are **naming** words.
Common nouns name things, e.g. the **cat** sat on the **table**. They also name abstract things, e.g. there was **anger** in her voice.
Proper nouns have capital letters and name people or places, e.g. **Julie** visited **Dublin**.

1. Write a suitable **noun** in each space in this story.

The Search

Once there was a little _____. There was a precious _____

hidden in the woods, so the little _____ went to look for it. Deep

between some dark _____ and gloomy _____ there was a

_____. The little _____ crept forward, frightened about

what might happen next. The _____ crunched and the

_____ swayed. The little _____ looked down and saw a

wonderful shiny _____! It was covered with _____ and

_____. The little _____ lifted it up and carried it carefully

_____.

2. Write a **common noun** that starts with each letter.

m _____   p _____   o _____

y _____   f _____   c _____

a _____   h _____   t _____

Turn over. Draw a map of Britain and label it with the names of ten towns. These are **proper nouns**.

Name _____   Date _____

Verbs

Verbs are **doing** words or **being** words, e.g. it **was** sunny so we **ran** and **played** outside.

1. Write a suitable **verb** in each space in this story.

The Pond

There _____ a pond in the park. Tony and Nicky _____ down the slope and _____ into the green depths. Nicky _____ on the mud and _____ into the water! His feet _____ covered with slime. Tony _____. Then Nicky _____ out of the pond and _____ up the bank. To his surprise, he _____ a frog lying in his jam jar. The boys _____ back across the park to _____ their friends the frog.

2. Write a **verb** that starts with each letter.

s _____   j _____   d _____

g _____   k _____   l _____

w _____   m _____   e _____

NOW   Write four different **verbs** about moving around a room.

_____   _____

_____   _____

Adjectives

Adjectives are **describing** words, e.g. a **fat** cat met a **frightened** mouse on a **cold, dark** night.

1. Write a suitable **adjective** in each space in this story.

Jack and the Beanstalk

Jack and his mother were _____. One _____ day,

Jack woke up to find a _____ beanstalk outside his

_____ window. Soon he was climbing up the _____

stalk, past the _____ leaves towards the _____ clouds.

Then he saw a _____ path leading to a _____ castle.

He knocked on the _____ door. A _____ giant opened the

door and Jack asked for some _____ food. He was given

_____ bread, and then the _____ giant fell asleep. Jack

quickly stole a _____ hen and some _____ gold, and

tumbled down the _____ beanstalk. Jack and his mother

were _____!

2. Write an **adjective** that starts with each letter.

n _____   g _____   i _____

t _____   r _____   h _____

e _____   m _____   s _____

NOW Write four **adjectives** to describe your friend.

_____   _____

_____   _____

Name _____   Date _____

Adverbs

Adverbs go with **verbs** to say **how** something is done, e.g. she performed **excellently**.
Many adverbs end in **ly**. Note the four common adverbs that do not follow this rule: **fast**, **well**, **soon** and **very**.

1. Write a suitable **adverb** in each space in this story.

The Disco

In one house, Shelley and Tammy were _____ looking forward to

going to the disco. They were getting ready _____. They were

_____ making choices – should it be skirts or leggings? Tammy

_____ tried on leggings and Shelley _____ chose a skirt.

Meanwhile, Aaron and Matt were setting off _____ for the hall.

The room _____ filled up and the lights went down _____.

The music pounded _____ and the dancers began _____ to

go on to the floor. Some people started the food _____, and soon

everyone was moving around _____.

2. Write an **adverb** that starts with each letter.

b _____   h _____   t _____

m _____   qu _____   p _____

NOW Imagine you are in each of these moods. Write an **adverb** to describe how you would come to school in each mood.

angry _____   happy _____

sad _____   sleepy _____

Name _____ Date _____

Prepositions

Prepositions show how one word **relates to** another, e.g. **in** the bottle, **out of** the bottle, **down** the throat.

1. Write a suitable **preposition** in each space in this story.

The Spectacular Stunts

The brave woman crashed _____ the ceiling _____ a

strong rope. There was a crystal _____ the ground

_____ her. It had strange writing _____ it. Suddenly,

sharp spikes popped _____ of the walls and began to dig

_____ her. She raced _____ two rocks, grabbed the

crystal and charged _____ the stairs. A boulder came

_____ her and she flattened herself _____ the rock wall.

The boulder went _____ and she was safe.

2. Write a **preposition** that starts with each letter.

b _____   o _____   a _____

t _____   f _____   u _____

n _____   w _____   i _____

Some **prepositions** go with other words, e.g. Jane **agreed with** her friend.

Write sentences using these words to show their meaning.

complain about _____

suffer from   _____

guilty of   _____

 # Conjunctions

Conjunctions are used to **connect** parts of sentences, e.g. this tree is an oak **and** so is this one.

1. Write a suitable **conjunction** in each space in this account. Try not to use **and** more than once.

The Thames Tunnel, London

The first tunnel under the Thames was begun in 1825, _____ was not completed _____ 1843. The river burst in twice _____ work had to stop. The engineer, called Mark Brunel, had to explore the flooded tunnel _____ find out how to repair it. He had invented a new 'shield' _____ there was not one for digging under water. This was then used, _____ men stood safe in the shield _____ they dug through holes in planks.

2. Write a sentence using each **conjunction**.

neither _____

however _____

therefore _____

although _____

either _____

Three **conjunctions** are used less often:

nevertheless   notwithstanding   despite

Check their meanings and usage in a dictionary. Turn over and write each one in a sentence.

Name _____   Date _____

Pronouns

A **pronoun** is a word which stands in place of a noun, e.g. tell **Rosie** the doctor will see **her** now. The word **her** is a **pronoun**, standing for the noun **Rosie**.

1. Write a suitable **pronoun** in each space in this story.

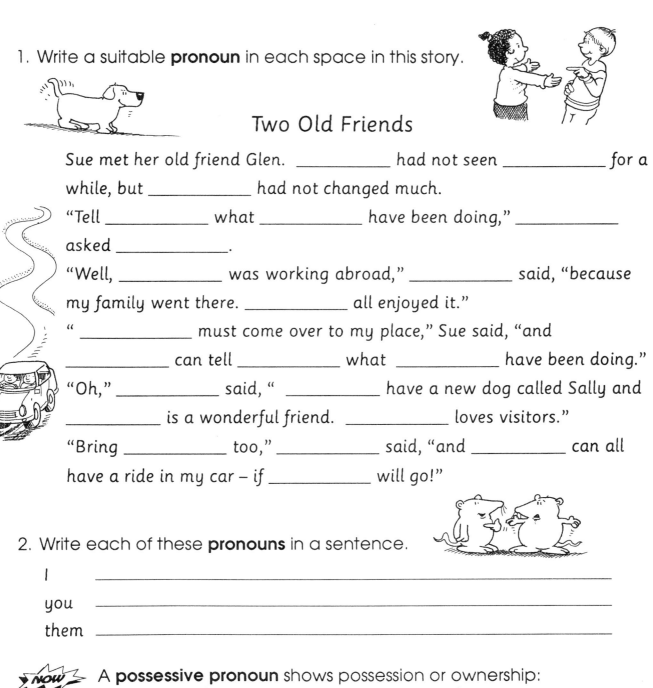

Two Old Friends

Sue met her old friend Glen. _____ had not seen _____ for a while, but _____ had not changed much.

"Tell _____ what _____ have been doing," _____ asked _____.

"Well, _____ was working abroad," _____ said, "because my family went there. _____ all enjoyed it."

" _____ must come over to my place," Sue said, "and _____ can tell _____ what _____ have been doing."

"Oh," _____ said, " _____ have a new dog called Sally and _____ is a wonderful friend. _____ loves visitors."

"Bring _____ too," _____ said, "and _____ can all have a ride in my car – if _____ will go!"

2. Write each of these **pronouns** in a sentence.

I _____

you _____

them _____

 A **possessive pronoun** shows possession or ownership:

hers   his   ours   mine   theirs   yours

Turn over and write these six possessive pronouns in six sentences.

Nouns, verbs, adjectives

1. **Nouns**. Nouns are names of **things**, **people** or **places**, e.g. **cat**, **Alexa**, **London**.

S						
U						
N						
S						
H						
I						
N						
E						

There are eight **nouns** in this story. Draw a line under each one and write it into the puzzle.

Natalie was by the sea. She sat under her umbrella and then decided to swim out of the harbour to an island. She sat in the sunshine and caught an eel in her net!

2. **Verbs**. Verbs are **doing** or **being** words, e.g. **go, drive, is, having**.

C						
A						
T						
C						
H						
I						
N						
G						

There are eight **verbs** in this story. Draw a line under each one and write it into the puzzle.

There is a television commercial which advertises coal fires. A cat comes into the room and tiptoes over to a dog. The cat cuddles up to the dog and the dog nuzzles the cat. Then a mouse hurries in and goes up to the cat and dog – all in front of a warm fire.

3. **Adjectives**. Adjectives are **describing** words, e.g. **red**, **old**, **your**.

F						
R						
I						
E						
N						
D						
L						
Y						

There are eight **adjectives** in this letter. Draw a line under each one and write it into the puzzle.

Dear Rob,
    Thanks for your interesting letter. Your new yellow bike sounds exciting! If the weather's fine tomorrow, let's go for a long relaxing ride.
                Your friend,
                Ahmed.

er Comparative and superlative adjectives

more

Comparative Adjectives

When we compare two things, we add **er** to the adjective,
e.g. small – small**er**. We write **more** in front of long adjectives,
e.g. incredible – **more** incredible.

1. Make these adjectives into **comparative adjectives**.

old _____	lucky _____
warm _____	hard _____
ancient _____	beautiful _____
fluffy _____	safe _____
short _____	thin _____

2. Choose two **comparative adjectives** and write them in two sentences.

_____

_____

Superlative Adjectives

When we compare three things or more, we add **est** to the adjective,
e.g. big – **biggest**. We put **most** in front of long adjectives,
e.g. dangerous - **most** dangerous.

1. Make these adjectives into **superlative adjectives**.

revolting _____	stupid _____
tuneful _____	happy _____
easy _____	straight _____
sad _____	colourful _____
early _____	speedy _____

Note: sometimes the adjective changes completely,
e.g. bad – **worse** – **worst**, good – **better** – **best**.

Present, past, future

Verbs are **doing** words or **being** words. **Verbs** say what **is** happening or what **has** happened, or what **will** happen.
We call this the **present tense**, **past tense**, or **future tense**.

Some Help

We usually form the simple past tense by adding **d** or **ed**, e.g. race – **raced**   jump – **jumped**.

We usually form the future tense by putting **shall** or **will** in front of the main verb, e.g. He **will** go away, I **shall** go fishing.
We use **shall** with **I** and **we**.
We use **will** with **she**, **he**, **it**, **you**, **they**.

1. Write these sentences in the **past tense**.

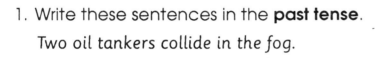

Two oil tankers collide in the fog.

_____

She receives top marks in the exam.

_____

I hand my bus pass to the conductor.

_____

2. Write these sentences in the **future tense**.

In the tunnel your voice echoed.

_____

I know we had a good time.

_____

Sue helps you if you have any problems.

_____

Many verbs are irregular when the past tense is formed, e.g. see – **saw**, grow – **grew**.

Turn over and write the past tense of these verbs:
bring   fly   give   go   win   write   swim   make   tell

Name _____ Date _____

Apostrophes

1. In each of these sentences, apostrophes have been missed out. Write them in the correct places.

The cat wasnt in its house.

Im going out as Ive got things to get.

Its 10 oclock so Ive got to rush.

Theyll have to get their coats as theyve got to keep their clothes dry.

Thats the one Ive always wanted!

Didnt you see that girls books?

I shant buy the boys game from him because I havent got the money.

It doesnt matter – we cant stay.

2. Make the **short forms** of these words and write them in four sentences.

should not   I will   it is   she is

_____

_____

_____

_____

Note: the only time you write **it's** is when you mean **it is** or **it has**. You do not use an apostrophe with **it** to show possession, e.g. **it's** hot (it is hot), the cat had **its** dinner (the dinner belongs to the cat).

Name _____   Date _____

Synonyms 1

Some words have similar meanings. They are called **synonyms**.

A word often used in writing is **said**.
Use other words in your writing in place of **said**.

1. Write these **synonyms** for **said** in alphabetical order:

agreed   stated   told   ordered   boasted   mentioned
        complained   suggested   announced   repeated
muttered   yelled   exclaimed   remarked   shouted

_____

_____

_____

_____

2. Choose four of the **synonyms** and write them in four sentences.

_____

_____

_____

_____

NOW Write a suitable said word in each space in these sentences.

"Does this train go to Liverpool?" she _____.

"I stole the sweet," _____ the child.

"I'm a very good reader," he _____.

"This is how it works!" she _____.

"Here we go, here we go, here we go," they _____.

"It's a secret!" he _____.

Name _____ Date _____

  # Synonyms 2

Some words have similar meanings. They are called **synonyms**.

1. Sort these happy verbs and sad verbs into two boxes.

complain   smile   groan   scowl   chuckle
    snigger   grieve   grumble   grin   sigh
moan   chortle   whinge   cackle   laugh
    giggle   whine   smirk   cheer   grizzle

happy		sad	

2. Write these four words into four sentences.
   cheered sobbed cackled muttered

_____

_____

_____

_____

 Some verbs can be used in different ways:

● we can **roar** with laughter or with anger

● we can **cry** when we are sad and **cry** out with pleasure

● we can **scream** with pain or with laughter.

Turn over and write three sentences using other
verbs that can be used in different ways.

Name _____ Date _____

Silent letters 1

Some Help

Only five of the letters of the alphabet are never silent: **f, j, q, v, x**.

Some common silent letters are:

w before **r**, e.g. **wrist**

k before **n**, e.g. **knock**

b after **m**, before **t**, e.g. **climb**, **debt**

l before **k, d, f,** or **m**, e.g. **talk**, **should**, **calf**, **palm**

c after **s**, e.g. **scissors**

t after **s**, e.g. **castle**

g before **h**, e.g. **light**

---

1. In this story, draw a line under the words with silent letters **w, k, b, l, c, t, g**. There are twenty-eight words to find.

She was writing about the ascent of a high mountain. 'I knew it would be tough – there was no doubt. It was frighteningly cold and every muscle ached. I wrapped my bright scarf tightly round me and then saw the summit scene in the half light. I climbed up, wrestling with the whistling wind which cut like a knife, and listening for the rustle of falling snow. Then there was a sudden calm and I walked up to the flag fastened to the icy rocks. I was delighted – until I thought about the fraught descent to come!'

2. Write the words you have found.

_____

_____

_____

_____

_____

Name _____ Date _____

Silent letters 2

Every vowel is silent at some time.

boat   lik**e**   tr**a**in   acti**o**n   g**u**est

The most common silent vowel is **e**.
This is sometimes called lazy **e** or magic **e**.

1. Write each pair of magic **e** words in the same sentence.

hate	stare

I hate it when people stare at me.

scrape	rake

_____

athlete	extreme

_____

slide	slime

_____

rode	slope

_____

use	cube

_____

2. Say these words aloud. Sort the words into the boxes.

juice	guard	build	cruise	fruit
guess	biscuit	suitable	tongue	pursuit

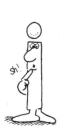

silent i
_____
_____
_____
_____
_____

silent u
_____
_____
_____
_____
_____

Name _____ Date _____

 # Proofreading 1

You should always read through and correct what you have written.
You need to look for incorrect spellings, and make sure your presentation
is clear.

In this account there are thirty-four incorrect spellings. As you read through,
draw a line under a spelling you think is incorrect. Check in a dictionary
and a book on prehistoric animals for the correct spellings.
Then write the correct spellings under the account.

  ## Prehistoric animals

Around 230 milion years ago was the age of the reptilles.

Some grew enoremous and were named dinosuars.

Some were plant-eeters and others were meet-eaters.

Brontosorus was a gental annimal which lived in

swomps. Tricerertops was an armored dinosuar which

ate tuff plants witch it choowed up with its sevennty

teath! Tyrranosaurus Rex was very feirce and was the

bigest meat-eatin dinosuar of all. Its largst teath were

thirtean centimeters long and as sharpe as dagers.

Nobody noes exackly how these gaint creachers dyed out.

_____

_____

_____

_____

_____

 FOLENS SPELLING – Reinforcement Activities Book 3 F5828

Proofreading 2

You should always read through and correct what you have written. You need to look for incorrect spellings, and make sure your presentation is clear.

In this account there are thirty-five incorrect spellings. As you read through, draw a line under a spelling you think is incorrect. Check in a dictionary for the correct spellings. Then write the correct spellings under the account.

Skyscrapers

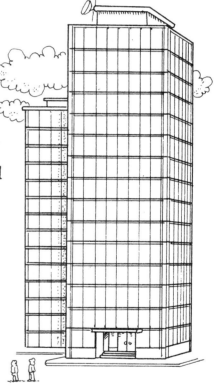

On the iland of Manhatton in New York are meny skyscrapers. Land to be developped is expencive and it is cheeper for biulders to build upwords. Bricks and morter are used for ordinery houses, but skyscrapers have to be construckted of concreet and steal for strenght. When it has metel rods in it, it is called reinforsed concreet. An arcitect desings the edifase and then excavaters with caterpiller tracks dig the fowndations. A surveyer makes a through investigashion, meashuring distanses with chayns, and angels with a theodilite. All these arangements are neccesary to insure the building is save.

_____

_____

_____

_____

_____

Name _____ Date _____

 # Proofreading 3

Sometimes you have to choose how to spell a word by what looks right.

1. Look at the groups of words. One spelling in each group is correct.
   Underline the correct spelling and write the word on the line
   next to the pair. If you are not sure, check in a dictionary.

er or or?

| visitor | _____ | inspector | _____ |
| visiter | | inspecter | |

| jewellor | _____ | passengor | _____ |
| jeweller | | passenger | |

| projector | _____ | bricklayor | _____ |
| projecter | | bricklayer | |

| conductor | _____ | traitor | _____ |
| conducter | | traiter | |

| doctor | _____ | director | _____ |
| docter | | directer | |

ary, ery or ory?   aw or au?

cemetary		laun	_____
cemetery	_____	lawn	
cemetory			

laboratary		saucer	_____
laboratery	_____	sawcer	
laboratory			

| | | dauning | _____ |
| | | dawning | |

dictionary			
dictionery	_____	daughter	_____
dictionory		dawghter	

machinary		aukward	_____
machinery	_____	awkward	
machinory			

| | | haunted | _____ |
| | | hawnted | |

FOLENS SPELLING – Reinforcement Activities Book 3 F5828   © Folens.

Name _____   Date _____

Letter strings

1. Write a pair of words next to each **letter string**.

(ice)	pol(ice)	not(ice)
sci	_____	_____
iour	_____	_____
eight	_____	_____
ough	_____	_____
ate	_____	_____
ure	_____	_____
ery	_____	_____
mn	_____	_____
ess	_____	_____
ally	_____	_____
rh	_____	_____
augh	_____	_____
ary	_____	_____
our	_____	_____

height   celebrate   dictionary

daughter   neighbour   business

rhythm   scissors

favourite   machinery

~~police~~   although

figure

science   autumn

weight   adventure

laugh   saviour

immediate   ~~notice~~

behaviour   mystery

rhyme

through

hymn   necessary

doubtless

physically   eventually

2. Write four words using these letter strings.

str	_____	_____	_____	_____
ion	_____	_____	_____	_____
ance	_____	_____	_____	_____
able	_____	_____	_____	_____
ment	_____	_____	_____	_____
ew	_____	_____	_____	_____
ary	_____	_____	_____	_____

Name _____   Date _____

Plurals 1

Some Help

Singular means one. **Plural** means more than one.
To make most nouns plural, just add **s**.
After a hissing sound add **es**.
Change **y** to **ies**, and change **f** (and sometimes **fe**) to **ves**.
Most nouns ending in **o** add **es**.
Do not use an apostrophe when making plurals.

1. Underline the correct spelling of the plural.
   Write the correct spelling at the end of each sentence.

The (leafs/leaves) turned brown.   _____

They played (dominos/dominoes).   _____

The (sopranos/sopranoes) sang well.   _____

I love (tomatos/tomatoes)!   _____

(Potatos/potatoes) make chips.   _____

Get out the (knifes/knives) and forks.   _____

He collects old (pennys/pennies).   _____

(Monkeys/monkies) are clever animals.   _____

The (roofs/rooves) had red tiles.   _____

She has some old (photos/photoes).   _____

"May I have some (matchs/matches)?"   _____

2. Some nouns are always in the plural form:

billiards	thanks	scissors	pliers
shorts	trousers	pincers	tweezers
measles	tongs	premises	pants

Choose four of these nouns and write them in four sentences.

_____

_____

_____

_____

Name _____   Date _____

   # Plurals 2

— Some Help —

Singular means one. **Plural** means more than one.
To make most nouns plural, just add **s**.
After a hissing sound add **es**.
Change **y** to **ies**, and change **f** (and sometimes **fe**) into **ves**.
Most nouns ending in **o** add **es**.
Do not use an apostrophe when making plurals.

There are some exceptions to these rules:
- some words are spelt **os** or **oes**, e.g. **banjos** or **banjoes**
- some words are spelt **fs** or **ves**, e.g. **scarfs** or **scarves**
- some words stay the same, e.g. **aircraft**, **salmon**, **sheep**
- some nouns change altogether in the plural, e.g. **die – dice**.

1. Write the plural form of these eight words in eight sentences.

family	video	sheep	woman
key	volcano	dwarf	watch

_____
_____
_____
_____
_____
_____
_____
_____

2. A **collective noun** is a naming word for groups of things,
   e.g. a **flock** of sheep.
   Write the **collective noun** for each of these groups:

A _____ of cattle.   A _____ of soldiers.
A _____ of bees.   A _____ of wolves.
A _____ of singers.   A _____ of planes.
A _____ of lions.   A _____ of people.

Name _____   Date _____

Homophones

Homophones are words which sound the same, but which are spelt
differently and have different meanings, e.g. they **wore** armour to go to **war**.

1. Write a word which sounds exactly like each of these words, but is
   spelt differently.

bored	_____board_____	scent	_____
steel	_____	stare	_____
warn	_____	meddle	_____
write	_____	whole	_____
allowed	_____	waist	_____
mined	_____	steak	_____
peace	_____	source	_____
sealing	_____	idol	_____

2. Write each pair of **homophones** in a sentence.

which
witch   _____

threw
through   _____

grown
groan   _____

áir
heir   _____

pair
pear   _____

bare
bear   _____

   Turn over and write a story using at
least five pairs of **homophones**.

Name _____   Date _____

Various vowel sounds

Some words have unusual vowel sounds.
Write the words in sentences.

1. Words with **o** which sounds like **u**, e.g. **money**.
   front   _____
   sponge   _____
   among   _____

2. Words with **y** which sounds like **i**, e.g. **pyjamas**.
   rhythm   _____
   mystery _____
   gym   _____

3. Words with **are** which sounds like **air**, e.g. **hare**.
   prepare   _____
   spare   _____
   nightmare _____

4. Words with **ar** which sounds like **or**, e.g. **dwarf**.
   reward   _____
   swarm   _____
   towards _____

5. Words with **a** which sounds like **o**, e.g. **watch**.
   wallet   _____
   warrant _____
   swamp   _____

6. Words with **ou** which sounds like **u**, e.g. **double**.
   trouble _____
   courage _____
   touch   _____

Spell **our** and **ear** words

Both of these letter strings can sound like **er**.

1. Sort these words into the two boxes.

learn	labour	search	flavour	early
journey	colour	pearl	vapour	heard
earnest	earth	odour	armour	

our	**ear**

2. Write these words in sentences.

humour _____

rehearse _____

journal _____

earthquake _____

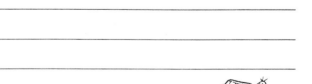

Use a dictionary to find the meanings of these words.

earnest _____

demeanour _____

search warrant _____

endeavour _____

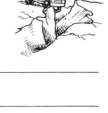

Name _____   Date _____

Spell eo, ia and io words

In some words which have two vowels together you can hear both vowels,
e.g. under the **neon** lights the **pianist** and the **violinist** played.

1. Sort these words into the three boxes.

diamond	onion	leotard	trio	lioness
neon	aerial	kiosk	diagram	peony
dial	video	radiator	geography	opinion
geometry	trial	violent		

eo	ia	io

2. Write these words in sentences.

diameter _____

riot _____

surgeon _____

initial _____

chariot _____

Use a dictionary to find the meanings of these words.

neolithic _____

judiciary _____

Spell **ph** words

When written together, **p** and **h** always say **f**,
e.g. I have a **ph**otogra**ph** of an ele**ph**ant.

1. Write the correct **ph** word in each sentence.

orphan   triumphant   phase   phrase   hyphen
emphasis   nephew   prophet   phenomenon

One who foretells events is a _____.

She made a _____ entrance.

A _____ can be used to join words or syllables.

A _____ is a stage of development or change.

A remarkable thing or occurrence is a _____.

A _____ is a small group of words.

An _____ is a child bereaved of parents.

He put great _____ on the words he spoke.

My sister's son is my _____.

2. Use a dictionary to find out what these people do:

A pharmacist   _____

A philosopher   _____

A photographer   _____

A phrenologist   _____

A physician   _____

A physiotherapist _____

  Turn over and write six sentences about these six jobs.

Abbreviations

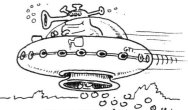

An abbreviation is a word that is shortened.
Sometimes only first letters of words are used.

1. Work out what these abbreviations stand for. Write the answer next to the abbreviation. Use the words in the box to help you.

U.N. _____

U.S.A. _____

N.A.S.A. _____

W.H.O. _____

U.N.E.S.C.O. _____

U.F.O. _____

N.A.T.O. _____

F.B.I. _____

R.A.M. _____

E.C. _____

Access	Cultural	Memory	Scientific
Administration	Educational	National	Space
Aeronautics	European	Nations	States
America	Federal	North	Treaty
Atlantic	Flying	Object	Unidentified
Bureau	Health	Organisation	United
Community	Investigation	Random	World

2. What do these abbreviations stand for?

e.g. _____ P.T.O. _____

etc. _____ P.S. _____

i.e. _____ R.S.V.P. _____

Polysyllabic words 1

┌─ Some Help ──────────────────

Polysyllabic words are words with many syllables.
They may be difficult to spell. Follow this system:
    Say the word slowly and carefully.
    Count the syllables.
    Divide the word into syllables.
    Cover the word.
    Write it from memory saying each syllable as you write,
    e.g. **qual/i/fi/ca/tion** = **qualification**.

1. Divide these words into syllables.
   Count the syllables and sort the words into boxes.

disappointing   graffiti   observatory   underdeveloped
         experiment   oxygen   fascinating   tarantula
longitude   electricity   instrument   determination

three syllables	four syllables	five syllables
_____	_____	_____
_____	_____	_____
_____	_____	_____
_____	_____	_____

2. We stress different syllables when we speak.
   Dictionaries show this by a stress mark ('),
   e.g. **ti´ger** – stress on first syllable, **volca´no** – stress on second syllable.
   Divide these words into syllables and write in the stress marks.

robot	torpedo	nylon	mistake
intend	private	December	robin
occur	electric	perfect	o'clock

Name _____   Date _____

Polysyllabic words 2

— Some Help —

Polysyllabic words are words with many syllables.
They may be difficult to spell. Follow this system:
    Say the word slowly and carefully.
    Count the syllables.
    Divide the word into syllables.
    Cover the word.
    Write it from memory saying each syllable as you write,
    e.g. **mis/un/der/stand/ing** = **misunderstanding**.

1. Divide these words into syllables and then spell them.

Word to learn	First try	Second try
autobiography	_____	_____
catastrophe	_____	_____
encyclopaedia	_____	_____
hypotenuse	_____	_____
microscopic	_____	_____
parallelogram	_____	_____
recommendation	_____	_____

2. Follow the same system with these names of nine countries.
   Divide each word into syllables. Cover the words and
   re-write them in alphabetical order.

Mozambique   Venezuela   Switzerland
Jamaica   Afghanistan   Israel
Nicaragua   Guatemala   Australia

_____

_____

_____

Anglo-Saxon words

The **Angles** came to the British Isles from Denmark, and the **Saxons** came from Holland and Germany. They first came in AD449. They called their language 'Englisc'.

1. In a dictionary, the letters **OE** show which words are Old English, or Anglo-Saxon. Read these words out loud first and then translate them into modern English.

Household words	
waeter	_____
foda	_____
duru	_____
buc	_____

Clothes	
socc	_____
scyrte	_____
haett	_____
glof	_____

Common words	
nama	_____
daeg	_____
todaeg	_____
aefter	_____
beforan	_____
behindan	_____
fram	_____
ofer	_____
bi	_____

2. Some Old English words are found in place names:
   ton or tun = village or enclosure
   ham = village or homestead
   wic = camp or dairy farm

Look in an atlas. Find some place names containing **ton**, **ham** or **wic**. Write the names.

_____

_____

_____

Name _____ Date _____

Prefixes from Latin

A **prefix** is a letter or group of letters at the beginning of a word which changes the way you use the word. You do not change the spelling of a word when you add a prefix.

─ Some Help ─

Here are some common prefixes and their meanings.

uni	= one	inter	= between
bi	= two	pre	= before
tri	= three	post	= after/behind
ad	= to/into	re	= back/again
ante	= before	super	= beyond/over
ex	= away from/out	tele	= far away

Write the meanings of these words.
Use a dictionary to check your answers.

unicorn _____

biennial _____

triplane _____

advance _____

ante-room _____

export _____

interject _____

preview _____

postscript _____

rebound _____

superpower _____

telepathy _____

 Turn over and write two words with each of these prefixes:

ab   contra   sub   trans

Prefixes from Greek

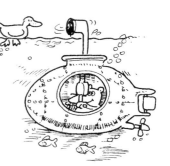

A **prefix** is a letter or group of letters at the beginning of a word which changes the way you use the word. You do not change the spelling of a word when you add a prefix.

┌ Some Help ─

Here are some common prefixes and their meanings.

chron	= to do with the time		mono	= one/single
peri	= around/about		therm	= heat
gen	= give birth to		auto	= self

Use a dictionary to find the meanings of these words. Write the meanings.

chronicle   _____

chronology   _____

perimeter   _____

periscope   _____

genetic   _____

genealogy   _____

monopoly   _____

monotonous   _____

thermal   _____

thermometer   _____

autobiography _____

autograph   _____

Turn over and write five sentences using five of these words.

Suffixes

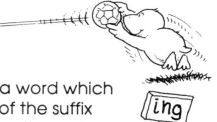

A **suffix** is a letter or group of letters at the end of a word which changes the way you use the word. The spelling of the suffix does not change, but the spelling of the word sometimes does.

⌐ Some Help ─────────────

Here are some common suffixes.

These suffixes usually make **nouns**:

ance	ence	age	ice	ly	
ure	ment	ism	er	or	ar
re	ness	hood	ship	dom	

These suffixes are often **verb** endings: ed ing ude ure yse ise ize

These suffixes usually make **adjectives**:

able	ful	al	y	like	ive
ous	ic	less	est	ary	ery
ory	ish	er			

Match each word with the correct suffix. Write the words.

govern	age	government
harm	ship	_____
king	ful	_____
child	ment	_____
friend	dom	_____
assist	less	_____
break	hood	_____
hero	ance	_____
post	able	_____
age	ism	_____

Turn over and write a word with each of these suffixes:

    ing   ous   ish   er   ence   ary

Name _____ Date _____

 # Suffixes from Greek 1

A **suffix** is a letter or group of letters at the end of a word which changes the way you use the word. The spelling of the suffix does not change, but the spelling of the word sometimes does.

1. When **ology** is added to a word it shows that it is to do with a subject of study. Use a dictionary to find out the meanings of these words:

   archaeology _____

   entomology _____

   etymology _____

   ornithology _____

   palaeontology _____

   psychology _____

   seismology _____

   speleology _____

   theology _____

   toxicology _____

2. When **cracy** is added to a word it shows that it is to do with government or ruling. Use a dictionary to find out the meanings of these words:

   aristocracy _____

   autocracy _____

   bureaucracy _____

   democracy _____

   plutocracy _____

   theocracy _____

3. **ism** makes abstract nouns.
   Use a dictionary to find out the meanings of these words:

   baptism _____

   heroism _____

Suffixes from Greek 2

A **suffix** is a letter or group of letters at the end of a word which changes the way you use the word. The spelling of the suffix does not change, but the spelling of the word sometimes does.

⌐ Some Help ─────────────────

Here are some common suffixes and their meanings.

gram	= written or drawn	phobia	=	horror
graph	= that which is written	ine	=	to do with
itis	= inflammation	onym	=	name

Use a dictionary to find the meanings of these words. Write the meanings.

anonymous _____

pseudonym _____

crystalline _____

quarantine _____

claustrophobia _____

agoraphobia _____

appendicitis _____

bronchitis _____

autograph _____

paragraph _____

diagram _____

program _____

Turn over and write five sentences using five of these words.

Name _____   Date _____

Using a dictionary 1

A **dictionary** explains the words of a language. The first major dictionary of the English Language was begun in 1747 by Dr. Samuel Johnson and six helpers, and was finished in 1755. He chose words he thought writers of the time should be using and decided what their meanings should be! Dictionaries today try to list all words used.

Here is an entry from a dictionary. The notes explain what everything stands for. They will help you use a dictionary properly.

This is the **main word** in bold type.

The letter **n.** is an abbreviation for **noun**. Other abbreviations include: **vb.** (verb), **adj.** (adjective), **adv.** (adverb), **prep.** (preposition), **conj.** (conjunction).

These signs tell you how to **say** the word:
– for a long vowel sound
ᴗ for a short vowel sound
′ shows where the stress goes.

This means the plural (**pl.**) can be made by adding **es**, or it can stay the same.

rhīnŏc ′ eros *n.* (*pl.* ~**es** or same). Large pachydermatous African and S. Asian quadruped with horn or two horns on nose and thick folded and plated skin; ~bird, ox-pecker; so **rhīnŏcerŏ ′ tic** *adj.* [ME, f.L f.Gk RHINO (*keros* f. *keras*, horn)].

This is the **meaning** of the word.

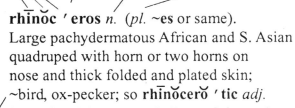

~ means another word which can be made from the main word. In this case, the **rhinoceros bird** is the ox-pecker.

Derivation – this tells you where the word comes from:
- **ME** (Middle English, AD1150–1500)
- **f.L** (from Latin)
- **f.Gk** (Greek – keros means 'horn').

Using a dictionary 2

Some words look similar or sound similar, but they have different meanings.
Use a dictionary to check the definitions of these similar words.
Write the meanings.

affect   _____
effect   _____

biannually _____
biennially _____

compliment _____
complement _____

continual   _____
continuous _____

dependant   _____
dependent   _____

elicit   _____
illicit   _____

lightening _____
lightning   _____

prescribe   _____
proscribe   _____

principal   _____
principle   _____

Choose one pair of words from the list.
Write each word in a sentence to show
the difference in meaning.

_____

_____

Using a thesaurus

A **thesaurus** contains a selection of words which are similar in meaning to a main word. The word thesaurus comes from the Greek, 'thesauros', which means treasure. Peter Mark Roget compiled the first thesaurus in 1805. It was published in 1852.

1. Use a thesaurus to find five words similar in meaning to each of these words.

fix   _____ _____ _____ _____ _____

clear   _____ _____ _____ _____ _____

go   _____ _____ _____ _____ _____

beautiful _____ _____ _____ _____ _____

jump   _____ _____ _____ _____ _____

hit   _____ _____ _____ _____ _____

2. These eight words have similar meanings to **said**.
   Write each word in a sentence to show its meaning.

   stated   insisted   ordered   explained
   remarked   boasted   announced   complained

_____

_____

_____

_____

_____

_____

_____

_____

 Use a thesaurus to find as many words as you can with a similar meaning to **good**. Turn over and write them.

Name _____   Date _____

Spell **ei** and **ie** words

1. Underline the correct spelling in these sentences.
   Write the correct word at the end of each sentence.

We paid the (casheir/cashier).   _____

The seats were in (teirs/tiers).   _____

The dog (seized/siezed) the bone.   _____

The (siege/seige) of the castle lasted a long time. _____

Her jacket was a (biege/beige) colour.   _____

He had a long (peice/piece) of string.   _____

The film was really (wierd/weird)!   _____

(Foreign/foriegn) means from another country. _____

The light shone from the (ceiling/cieling).   _____

The alphabet (frieze, freize) was on the wall. _____

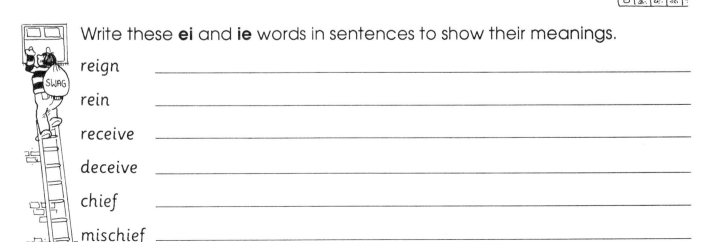

Write these **ei** and **ie** words in sentences to show their meanings.

reign _____

rein _____

receive _____

deceive _____

chief _____

mischief _____

Name _____   Date _____

 # Spell **ew**, **ue** and **ui** words

The letters **ew**, **ue** and **ui** can make an **oo** sound:

The **cruiser** came into **view**, but it was **overdue**.

1. Underline the correct spelling in these sentences.
   Write the correct spelling at the end of each sentence.

The (jewel, juel, juil) sparkled.   _____

It was a (trew, true, trui) story.   _____

I love orange (jewce, juece, juice).   _____

He had a bad (brewse, bruese, bruise).   _____

She was very (shrewd, shrued, shruid).   _____

The (yew, yue, yui) tree grew tall.   _____

The hot (grewel, gruel, gruil) was tasty.   _____

She was a new (recrewt, recruet, recruit).   _____

They fought a (dewel, duel, duil).   _____

He went on a (crewse, cruese, cruise).   _____

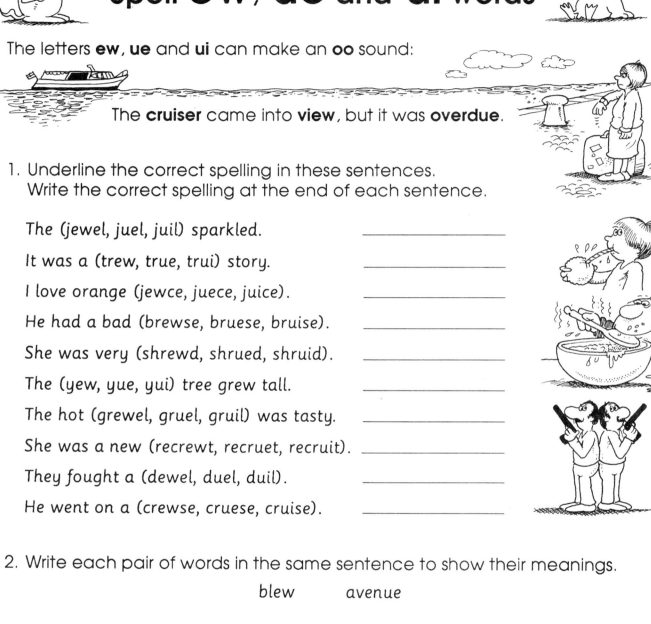

2. Write each pair of words in the same sentence to show their meanings.

blew	avenue

_____

knew	view

_____

continue	cruise

_____

threw	glue

_____

Spell le, al and el words

Some Help

Most short common words ending in an **l** sound take the ending
le. Longer words may take **al**, because in English you cannot
have words ending in **mle**, **rle** or **nle**, nor **cle** if the **c** is soft.
The ending **el** is not very common.

---

1. Underline the correct spelling in these sentences.
   Write the correct spelling at the end of each sentence.

The car was not very (reliable, reliabal, reliabel). _____

Each dress had a (lable, labal, label). _____

The road was full of (vehicles, vehicals, vehicels). _____

She drew a (horizontle, horizontal, horizontel) line. _____

The shops are (locle, local, locel). _____

She wrote an (article, artical, articel) for the paper. _____

Our car went through the (tunnle, tunnal, tunnel). _____

He was rushed to (hospitle, hospital, hospitel). _____

I love (caramle, caramal, caramel)! _____

She bought him a (specile, special, speciel) present. _____

2. A few words end in **ol** or **il**. Put these words into sentences.

gerbil _____

pupil _____

vigil _____

gambol _____

idol _____

pistol _____

Spell **ate**, **ite** and **ete** words

The ending **ate** is common.
The endings **ite** and **ete** are less common.

1. Underline the correct spelling in these sentences.
   Write the correct spelling at the end of each sentence.

   The wind was (moderate, moderite). _____

   They swam to (opposete, opposite) ends. _____

   The ring was (exquisate, exquisite). _____

   Blue is my (favourate, favourite) colour. _____

   The design was (elaborate, elaborite). _____

   She got a (certificate, certificite). _____

   The builders used (concrate, concrete). _____

   It was a (definate, definite) answer. _____

   The mistake was (deliberite, deliberate). _____

   It was hard to (complite, complete). _____

2. Use a dictionary to find the meanings of these words.
   Write the meanings.

   literate _____

   radiate _____

   gelignite _____

   concrete _____

   trilobite _____

   NOW Turn over and make as many words as possible out of **demonstrate**.
   The words must have three letters or more – but no plurals!.
   More than thirty words = good.
   More than fifty words = very good!

Spell **ant** and **ent** words

The ending **ent** is more common than **ant**.
They are usually used for adjectives.

1. Underline the correct spelling in these sentences.
   Write the correct spelling at the end of each sentence.

She was (confidant/confident) of winning.   _____

The play was (brillient/brilliant).   _____

The (patient/patiant) was very sick.   _____

Do not be (ignorent/ignorant) of the law!   _____

He said he was (innocant/innocent).   _____

It was an (important/importent) choice.   _____

The glass was (transparent/transparant).   _____

We spoke to the (attendant/attendent).   _____

She was an (independant/independent) person.   _____

The football score was (magnificant/magnificent)!   _____

2. Many words end in **ment**. Write a short story
   which includes all these **ment** words:

moment	excitement	payment	equipment
monument	pavement	experiment	agreement

   _____

   _____

   _____

   _____

   _____

   _____

   _____

   _____

Turn over to continue your story.

Name _____ Date _____

Spell **ance** and **ence** words

The ending **ence** is more common than **ance**.
They are usually used for nouns.

1. Underline the correct spelling in these sentences.
   Write the correct spelling at the end of each sentence.

   We could not see any (difference/differance). _____

   She had lots of (confidance/confidence). _____

   We came to their (assistance/assistence). _____

   Drivers must have car (insurence/insurance). _____

   We noted their (absence/absance). _____

   It was a strange (substence/substance). _____

   He was a good (influance/influence). _____

   We liked its (appearance/appearence). _____

   It was hard to keep our (balence/balance). _____

   It was a serious (offence/offance). _____

2. These verbs can be made into nouns by adding **ence** or **ance**.
   Take care – some verbs change their form when they become nouns.
   The first one is done for you.

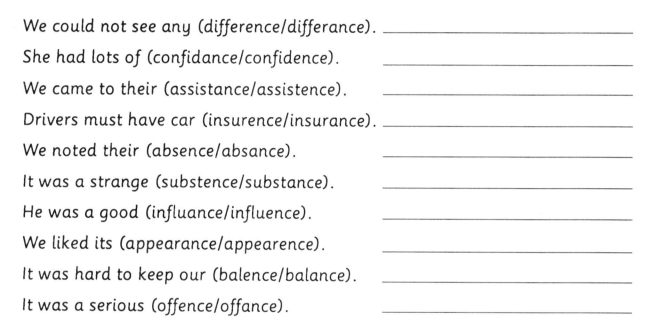

appear	–	_appearance_
assist	–	_____
excel	–	_____
ignore	–	_____
differ	–	_____
exist	–	_____
insure	–	_____

FOLENS SPELLING – Reinforcement Activities Book 3 F5828   © Folens.

Name _____   Date _____

 # Alphabet game

Each player fills in the boxes with suitable words beginning with each letter.
When all the boxes are filled in, points can be awarded:
  one point if someone else has the same word
  five points if nobody else has the same word.

The more unusual words you can think of, the more points you will score!
The winner is the player with the most points at the end of the game.

	Girl's name	Boy's name	Occupation	Food	Country
a	Anna	Ahmed	artist	apple pie	Austria
b					
c					
d					
e					
f					
g					
h					
i					
j					
k					
l					
m					
n					
o					
p					
q					
r					
s					
t					
u					
v					
w					
x					
y					
z					

Name _____   Date _____

 Sumeo **Jumbled words** drib

1. Work out these jumbled words. Write the answers on the lines.

Fruit	
leapp	_____
reap	_____
onelm	_____
sperag	_____
mulp	_____
greano	_____
nabaan	_____
byesarrrp	_____

Vegetables	
tootap	_____
sape	_____
saben	_____
clearifullow	_____
tarroc	_____
tootam	_____
clerey	_____
shrida	_____

Trees	
sha	_____
chebe	_____
pleam	_____
yollh	_____
rif	_____

Clothes	
toca	_____
slegov	_____
stobo	_____
teckaj	_____
sneriart	_____

2. When a jumbled word makes a proper word it is called an **anagram**:

   live = evil   stake = steak   dear = dare

Turn over and make up some anagrams for a friend to work out.

 NOW Sometimes names can be changed:
 toga   Florence Nightingale =   flit on cheering angel
          Winston Churchill =   crunch not his will!
       Make an anagram of your name.

rat bib

FOLENS SPELLING – Reinforcement Activities Book 3 F5828   © Folens.

Word puzzles

1. There are eight words joined together in this line.
   There are also twenty-three other words hidden in the line.
   All the words go from left to right.

   ## comfortableelectrickingotterraceservergermanaged

   Find the eight key words and write them here.

   _____

   _____

   Find the twenty-three other words and write them here.

   _____

   _____

   _____

   _____

   _____

2. There are eleven words in this line, each with six letters.
   All the words go from left to right.
   Sort them out and write them on the lines.

   ## combatherballethalvespermittenantler

   _____   _____   _____   _____

   _____   _____   _____   _____

   _____   _____   _____

3. Join these four words in one line to make
   three new six letter words.
   The first two words have been joined for you.

   ### carton   ledges   gerbil   silver

   cartonsilver

   _____

Wordsearch 1

Britain in World War Two

Find these words in the wordsearch.
The words go in any direction.

EVACUATION	SHELTERS	SANDBAGS	GASMASKS
WIRELESS	BLACKOUT	AIR RAID	POSTERS
RATIONING	BLITZ	BOMBS	HOME GUARD
TANK	GUNS	DUNKIRK	VE DAY
VJ DAY	VICTORY	PEACE	

R	I	K	B	D	U	N	K	I	R	K	E	D
R	I	G	O	L	I	N	Y	R	Y	P	P	G
A	V	H	M	O	A	R	O	T	C	A	E	A
T	O	O	B	T	O	C	V	I	C	E	A	S
I	E	O	S	T	V	S	K	V	N	P	C	M
O	L	D	C	I	E	R	J	O	B	O	E	A
N	K	I	R	K	S	E	I	C	U	S	Z	S
I	V	A	V	N	G	T	U	I	B	T	G	K
N	Y	R	J	G	A	L	R	V	I	E	U	S
G	A	R	U	U	B	E	N	L	O	R	N	T
L	D	I	C	N	D	H	B	O	M	S	T	U
T	E	A	R	S	N	S	V	J	D	A	Y	N
I	V	D	D	R	A	U	G	E	M	O	H	S
E	O	V	V	O	S	S	E	L	E	R	I	W

Make up your own wordsearch to include the names of six leaders from World War Two.

 FOLENS SPELLING – Reinforcement Activities Book 3 F5828   © Folens.

Name _____   Date _____

Wordsearch 2

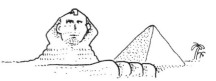

1. Ancient Egypt

Find these Egyptian words in the wordsearch. The words go in any direction.

TUTANKHAMUN
RA
STATUE
PHARAOH
NUT
BEADS
SET
ISIS
HORUS
ANKESENUM
CARTER

GOLD
VASES
THRONE
SEALS
MASK
ANUBIS
THOTH
OSIRIS
MUMMY
SPHINX
CAIRO

S	P	T	U	S	P	H	I	N	X	T	U	M
H	T	M	U	M	M	Y	T	U	T	N	M	U
T	N	R	S	L	A	E	S	T	U	T	M	N
O	O	E	U	M	A	R	U	M	U	D	T	E
H	S	S	S	S	E	S	A	V	T	L	U	S
T	I	T	I	E	P	H	A	R	A	O	H	E
E	R	C	U	S	K	H	S	P	I	G	S	K
N	I	A	N	N	I	N	H	I	R	X	D	N
O	S	R	A	U	K	S	A	M	I	N	A	A
R	S	T	A	T	U	E	X	P	S	S	E	T
H	U	E	C	A	I	R	O	T	O	U	B	T
T	K	R	S	I	A	N	U	B	I	S	I	S

S	L	A	T	I	L	E	S	L	A	I	V	I
Y	A	L	C	A	L	F	O	R	U	M	I	I
V	E	S	I	A	A	R	E	S	S	L	L	L
L	I	T	N	L	T	R	V	R	L	C	L	L
A	L	E	U	L	A	I	O	A	T	O	G	A
W	B	S	T	I	L	T	A	M	H	S	L	M
O	G	A	A	V	A	L	I	V	E	G	O	O
D	O	S	C	I	F	O	R	N	A	O	O	S
S	O	L	D	U	I	L	B	A	T	H	S	A
M	D	A	A	V	S	D	O	G	R	L	C	I
G	L	S	C	H	O	O	L	S	E	S	H	C
G	R	E	A	F	O	R	O	A	D	S	I	C

2. The Romans in Britain

Find these Roman words in the wordsearch. The words go in any direction.

ROME
LATIN
GLADIATORS
THEATRE
TOGA
TUNIC
SCHOOL
LAW
ABACUS

BATHS
FORUM
ROADS
MOSAIC
VILLA
CLAY
TILES
GODS

Name _____ Date _____

Crossword making

You will need two copies of this sheet – one rough, one neat.

1. On the rough copy, write words across and down to fit in the spaces. Make up clues for the words.
2. On the neat copy, just write the clues. Give the crossword to a friend to complete.

Note: The numbers in brackets are the number of letters in each word.

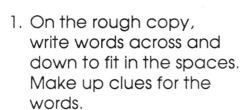

1		2			3	4		5	
			6						
		7							
8		9			10	11			
12	13		14				15		
16				17					

Across

1. _____ (4)
3. _____ (4)
6. _____ (2)
7. _____ (6)
8. _____ (4)
10. _____ (4)
13. _____ (6)
16. _____ (4)
17. _____ (4)

Down

1. _____ (6)
2. _____ (4)
4. _____ (4)
5. _____ (6)
6. _____ (3)
9. _____ (5)
11. _____ (5)
12. _____ (3)
14. _____ (2)
15. _____ (3)

Make up another crossword using longer words.

Expand your vocabulary 1

Analogies show relationships between words:

boy is to **man** as **girl** is to **woman**.

Choose a word from the list which is related to the boxed word in each sentence. Write the word to complete the analogy.

synonym	symphony	vessel
lake	vixen	atrocious
leveret	gosling	atoll
abhor	sensible	taciturn

Stream is to river as |pond| is to _____

Dog is to bitch as |fox| is to _____

Noisy is to voluble as |quiet| is to _____

Horse is to foal as |hare| is to _____

Goat is to kid as |goose| is to _____

Opposite is to antonym as |same| is to _____

Good is to excellent as |bad| is to _____

Love is to adore as |hate| is to _____

Chapter is to novel as |movement| is to _____

Lorry is to vehicle as |ship| is to _____

Mad is to sane as |silly| is to _____

Moon is to corona as |lagoon| is to _____

Write two analogies of your own.

_____

_____

Expand your vocabulary 2

These are difficult words to spell.
They are also difficult to understand!

Write each of the words on a line with its meaning.
Use a dictionary to help you.

camouflage	yoghurt	esoteric	vacuum
mauve	naive	chaos	nuance
piranha	suave	euphemism	conscientious
casualty	static	precocious	harangue

_____

_____

_____

_____

_____

_____

_____

_____

_____

_____

_____

_____

_____

_____

_____

_____

_____

_____